Holly's
First Day at
School

by **Sarah, Duchess of York**
Illustrated by Ian Cunliffe

Holly's First Day at School

helping hand books

First published in Great Britain 2007 by Lloyds Pharmacy Ltd
Sapphire Court, Walsgrave Triangle, Coventry CV2 2TX

www.lloydspharmacy.com

In consultation with Cameron Wilson Ltd

Illustrated by Ian Cunliffe

'Ten Helpful Hints' contributed by Dr. Richard Woolfson,
child psychologist, Fellow of the British Psychological Society.

Printed in China

British Library Cataloguing in Publication Data
A catalogue record for this book is available from the British Library

ISBN 978-1-906260-03-3

All children face many new experiences as they grow up and helping them to understand and deal with each is one of the most demanding and rewarding things we do as parents. The helping hand books are for both children and parents to read, perhaps together. Each simple story describes a childhood experience and shows some of the ways in which to make it a positive one. I do hope these books encourage children and parents to talk about these sometimes difficult issues; talking together goes a long way to finding a solution.

Sarah, Duchess of York

Holly couldn't stop talking. She had so many things she wanted to tell her Mummy.

"And then we went to the playground! And Manya came too! Manya's my new friend!" she said, hardly taking a breath.

"You'll like her, Mummy.

And we played Hopscotch."

"And then we had drawing.
I haven't finished my drawing
yet but I'm going to do some more tomorrow.
Mrs Anderson says she likes my picture.
I just need to add more colours."

Holly had so many things to say that they were
home before her Mummy could get a word in.

"Well, I'm glad that you had such a busy day,
Holly. I told you this morning that it was going to
be exciting."

Holly thought back to that morning and how she had felt. It seemed such a long time ago now.

She had been unhappy and a little frightened. She liked being at home with her Mummy and Jake, her baby brother, and now she was going to have to spend some of every day away from them.

Mummy and Daddy had taken her to the school a few weeks ago so that she could see where it was and meet Mrs Anderson, the teacher.

They had only been able to stay for a little while and Mummy and Daddy had been with her all the time so it wasn't the same as being there on her own.

Holly had talked to Amy, her friend Charlotte's big sister, who had been at the school for two years.

"It's great," Amy had said, "you'll make lots of friends and Mrs Anderson is quite fun. Except for when she asks you to do 'Sums'. I don't like 'Sums'."

Holly thought she wouldn't like doing 'Sums' either but she loved the idea of some new friends.

That first morning, it still all seemed very strange and although Holly was not the sort of girl who cried – baby Jake did enough of that for both of them! – she had felt tears in her eyes as her Mummy had squeezed her hand at the school gates and said, "You go with Mrs Anderson now. I shall be back this afternoon before you know it!"

Holly joined lots of other children who looked just as lost as she did.

Mrs Anderson guided them along the corridor to the school's assembly hall. The hall was big and noisy, full of children talking to one another and all of them seemed to be older than Holly.

A tall man walked into the room, clapped his hands and everyone stopped talking.
"Good morning children,"
said the man who Holly knew was the head teacher, Mr Wainwright.

"Welcome back to school. I hope you enjoyed the holidays. I know I did ! And a special welcome to the children who are joining us this term. I hope you will be very happy here."

After assembly, Mrs Anderson took all the children to their classroom which Holly remembered from the time she had come before. It was a big room with lots of windows. Holly could see the playground outside.

It had white walls, little wooden tables, blue chairs and, in one corner, a huge pile of building bricks. On the walls were pinned lots of colourful things. There was a big poster with all the different letters of the alphabet and a picture by each one, A is for Apple and so on.

On another wall were
some children's drawings.

Mrs Anderson explained that they had been
done by last year's class but she thought they
made the room seem brighter until the children
had some pictures of their own to put up. There
were drawings of cows, dogs, houses, trees and
one of a very large bumble bee which made
Holly shiver!

"First, we'll all sit in a circle and get to know each other," said Mrs Anderson.

When they had sat down, she went round everyone asking them their names and where they lived.

Holly discovered that her new friend, Manya, lived just round the corner from her.

They would be able to play together!

The rest of the day passed in a whirl: reading, playing, lunchtime and, Holly's favourite, drawing.

"What are you going to draw, Holly?" asked Mrs Anderson.

"How about the playground?"

Holly looked out of the window and was soon busy with her pencil. So busy in fact that, before she knew it, it was time to go home.

Holly was one of the last to come out of school as she had been busy putting her pencils away.

"Are you alright, Holly?" asked her Mummy, who had been waiting at the school gates for some time and was becoming a little anxious.

"Mummy, I'm fine," said Holly. "Can I come back tomorrow?"

Then, without stopping, Holly began to tell her mummy everything about her busy first day at school!

TEN HELPFUL HINTS
FOR PARENTS OF CHILDREN WHO ARE
STARTING SCHOOL by Dr. Richard Woolfson

1. Don't use school as a threat when your pre-schooler misbehaves. That gets things off on the wrong footing, and your child will begin to dislike the thought of school even before she has set eyes on it.

2. Let your child ask you questions. In the months running up to that first day at school, she'll probably ask you what it will be like, about the staff and the other children. This is only natural. Answer all her questions as best you can.

3. Arrange visits to the school. Take her there on a visit at least once before she starts attending regularly. If her nursery doesn't arrange this, make contact with your local school directly.

4. Encourage your child to look round the whole school, not just her classroom. She should view, for instance, the dining area, the toilets, the playground and the assembly hall. The more she is able to walk round the entire school, the better.

5. Get her used to group activities. In the classroom, most learning takes place in group settings and the more experience of this that your child has before she starts school the better. Provide opportunities for her to play with other children her own age at group games and group activities. This prepares her for what lies ahead in class.

6. Sharpen her independence skills. Practice the key tasks that she'll need to cope with every day in school, such as taking turns, putting on her coat, completing basic activities without needing attention, managing on her own in the toilet, answering questions, fastening her shoes and clothes, and eating tidily at the table.

7. Keep her confidence high. Boost your child's confidence for starting school by reassuring her that she is a very capable child and that she'll do well at school. Point out her strengths to her. Tell her that the other children will all like her and will want to be her friend.

8. Remain calm on the first day. Your child's starting school is also a significant event in your own life and some parents get upset on the first day when separating from their child at school. Try to stay relaxed and happy when taking her there as she will follow your lead.

9. Always be enthusiastic when talking about school. Your child is heavily influenced by your attitudes and values. So if you have a positive and upbeat approach when talking with her about school, the chances are that she will be enthusiastic as well.

10. When you collect her from the infant school at the end of the first day, ask her lots of questions about what happened there. Give her lots of time to chatter away to you, and respond positively. If she has any concerns at all, give an instant response to show that they can be easily resolved.

The helping hand books

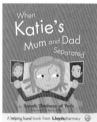

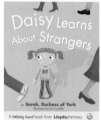

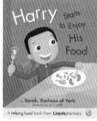

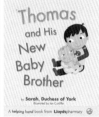

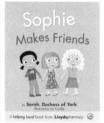

Lloydspharmacy